WORDS THEIR WAY®

WORD STUDY IN ACTION • LETTER NAME

Glenview, Illinois

Boston, Massachusetts

Chandler, Arizona

Upper Saddle River, New Jersey

ALWAYS LEARNING

PEARSON

Photographs

Every effort has been made to secure permission and provide appropriate credit for photographic material. The publisher deeply regrets any omission and pledges to correct errors called to its attention in subsequent editions.

Unless otherwise acknowledged, all photographs are the property of Pearson Education, Inc.

Photo locators denoted as follows: Top (T), Center (C), Bottom (B), Left (L), Right (R), Background (Bkgd)

Cover (B) Seiya Kawamoto/Thinkstock, (T) Jupiterimages/Thinkstock, (BL) Design Pics/Michael Interisano/Thinkstock; **1** (Roof) ©AbleStock/Index Open, (Road) ©Alexey Stiop/Shutterstock, (Monkey) ©Eric Isselée/Shutterstock, (Bear) ©Eric Isselée/Shutterstock, (Sink) ©Simple Stock Shots, (Rocket) Comstock Images/Thinkstock, (Map) Digital Wisdom, Inc., (Seal) ImageShop/Jupiter Images, (Baby) Jupiter Images, (Mouse) Photos to Go/Photolibrary, (Barn) Shutterstock, (Band) Thinkstock; **3** (Saw) Getty Images, (Mop) Stockbyte/Thinkstock; **4** (Saw) Getty Images, (Mop) Stockbyte/Thinkstock; **5** (Pig) ©Anat-oli/Shutterstock, (Walnut) ©M. Unal Ozmen/Shutterstock, (Peach) ©Nikolai Pozdeev/Shutterstock, (Tire) ©photolibrary/Index Open, (Game) ©Tatik22/Shutterstock, (Nurse) Dynamic Graphics/Thinkstock, (Pan, Nail) Getty Images, (Goose) Hemera Technologies, (Gold) Photodisc/Thinkstock, (Tooth) Shutterstock, (Gate) Thinkstock; **7** (Safety Pin) ©Ablestock/Index Open, (Goat) ©Eric Isselée/Shutterstock, (Nest) Jupiter Images; **8** (Safety Pin) ©Ablestock/Index Open, (Goat) ©Eric Isselée/Shutterstock, (Nest) Jupiter Images; **9** (Fish) ©Eric Isselée/Shutterstock, (Hen, Fire) Getty Images, (Dinosaur) Hemera Technologies, (Feather) Jupiter Images, (Hill, Camel) Photos to Go/Photolibrary, (Duck) Shutterstock, (Hay, Ham, Deer, Cape) Thinkstock; **11** (Hat) ©Heath Doman/Shutterstock, (Fox) ©Jeremy Woodhouse/Getty Images, (Can) Thinkstock; **12** (Hat) ©Heath Doman/Shutterstock, (Fox) ©Jeremy Woodhouse/Getty Images, (Can) Thinkstock; **13** (Waves, Lion, Kitten, Kitchen, Kangaroo, Eagle) Getty Images, (Jet) Photos to Go/Photolibrary, (Web, Lizard, King) Thinkstock; **15** (Kite) ©D. Hurst/Alamy, (Leaf) ©Royalty-Free/Corbis, (Jeep) Photos to Go/Photolibrary; **16** (Kite) ©D. Hurst/Alamy, (Leaf) ©Royalty-Free/Corbis, (Jeep) Photos to Go/Photolibrary, (Zebra) Shutterstock, (Vine) Thinkstock; **17** (Volcano, Violin) Getty Images, (Zoo, Yard) Photos to Go/Photolibrary, (Zebra) Shutterstock, (Vine) Thinkstock; **21** (Hat) ©Heath Doman/Shutterstock, (Bat) Getty Images, (Rat) Jupiterimages/Thinkstock, (Can) Thinkstock; **25** (Mad) ©Brazhnykov Andriy/Shutterstock, (Dad) ©Corbis, (Can) Thinkstock; **29** (Map) Digital Wisdom, Inc., (Nap) Photos to Go/Photolibrary; **33** (Dad) ©Corbis, (Nap) Photos to Go/Photolibrary; **37** (Frog) ©Malcolm Schuyl/Alamy, (Pot) ©Margouillat Photo/Shutterstock, (Log) ©Sebastian Knight/Shutterstock, (Hot) ©Simone van den Berg/Alamy, (Hog) ©Tim Burrett/Shutterstock, (Cot) Hemera Technologies, (Mop) Stockbyte/Thinkstock; **41** (Pig) ©Anat-oli/Shutterstock, (Mill) Photos to Go/Photolibrary, (Dig) Shutterstock, (Rip) Thinkstock; **45** (Walnut) ©M. Unal Ozmen/Shutterstock, (Run) ©Monkey Business Images/Shutterstock, (Bug) Brand X Pictures/Thinkstock, (Hut) Photos to Go/Photolibrary; **49** (Men) ©Gemenacom/Shutterstock, (Hen) Getty Images, (Jet) Photos to Go/Photolibrary, (Wet, Beg) Thinkstock; **57** (Ship) ©DesignsPics/Index Open, (Shadow) ©Igor Kovalchuk/Shutterstock, (Chick) Getty Images, (Chimney) Thinkstock; **59** (Sheep) Getty Images, (Cherry) Photos to Go/Photolibrary; **60** (Sheep) Getty Images, (Cherry) Photos to Go/Photolibrary; **61** (Thorn) ©Evgeni S./Shutterstock, (Wheelbarrow) ©James M. Phelps, Jr./Shutterstock, (Whale) ©Royalty-Free/Corbis, (Wheat) ©Zeljko Radojko/Shutterstock, (Thermos) Photos to Go/Photolibrary; **65** (Ship) ©DesignsPics/Index Open, (Thorn) ©Evgeni S./Shutterstock, (Wheelbarrow) ©James M. Phelps, Jr./Shutterstock, (Whale) ©Royalty-Free/Corbis, (Chick) Getty Images, (Thermos) Photos to Go/Photolibrary; **67** (Sheep) Getty Images; **68** (Sheep) Getty Images; **69** (Tire) ©photolibrary/Index Open, (Tiger) ©Smit/Shutterstock, (Saw) Getty Images, (Seal) ImageShop/Jupiter Images, (Stove) Shutterstock; **71** (Sink) ©Simple Stock Shots, (Tooth) Shutterstock; **72** (Sink) ©Simple Stock Shots, (Tooth) Shutterstock; **73** (Spill) ©Barbara Quinn/Shutterstock, (Smell) ©OJO Images Ltd./Alamy, (Spout) Comstock Images/Thinkstock, (Spear) Hemera Technologies/Thinkstock, (Smoke) Index Open, (Spider, Dogs) Photos to Go/Photolibrary, (Skiis) Shutterstock, (Sky, Skunk) Thinkstock; **77** (School) ©David R. Frazier Photolibrary, Inc./Alamy Images, (Scale) ©Luis Louro/Shutterstock, (Scooter) Comstock Images/Thinkstock, (Swing, Swim, Snake) Getty Images, (Snail) Jupiter Images, (Swan, Snow) Photos to Go/Photolibrary, (Snowman) Thinkstock; **79** (Scarecrow) Brand X Pictures/Thinkstock, (Swan) Photos to Go/Photolibrary; **80** (Scarecrow) Brand X Pictures/Thinkstock, (Swan) Photos to Go/Photolibrary; **81** (Plow) ©Andrew Holt/Getty Images, (Sleep) ©Corbis Super RF/Alamy, (Flowers) ©Tony Lilley/Alamy, (Plum) ©Valentyn Volkov/Shutterstock, (Flute, Blanket) Getty Images, (Slice) Photos to Go/Photolibrary, (Float) Thinkstock; **83** (Plate) ©Artur Synenko/Shutterstock, (Fly) John Foxx/Thinkstock; **84** (Plate) ©Artur Synenko/Shutterstock, (Fly) John Foxx/Thinkstock; **85** (Grasshopper) ©Creatas, (Crane) ©Phant/Shutterstock, (Clouds) ©Royalty-Free/Corbis, (Frame) ©Valentin Agapov/Shutterstock, (Crown) Corbis/Jupiter Images, (Frying Pan) Jupiter Images, (Freezer) Shutterstock, (Grass, Crib) Stockdisc, (Claw) Thinkstock; **87** (Frog) ©Malcolm Schuyl/Alamy, (Crab) Getty Images, (Clown) Thinkstock; **88** (Frog) ©Malcolm Schuyl/Alamy, (Crab) Getty Images, (Clown) Thinkstock; **89** (Tree) ©Borislav Gnjidic/Shutterstock, (Dream) ©Giuseppe R/Shutterstock, (Dream) ©Ivonne Wierink/Shutterstock, (Prince) ©Kitti/Shutterstock, (Tracks) ©Royalty-Free/Corbis, (Prize) Comstock/Thinkstock, (Bridge) Corbis, (Princess) Digital Vision/Thinkstock, (Bread) Hemera Technologies, (Drill) Shutterstock, (Dragon, Bride) Thinkstock; **91** (Train) ©Jupiterimages/Thinkstock/Alamy; **92** (Train) ©Jupiterimages/Thinkstock/Alamy; **93** (Kite) ©D. Hurst/Alamy, (Wheelbarrow) ©James M. Phelps, Jr./Shutterstock, (Whale) ©Royalty-Free/Corbis, (Wheat) ©Zeljko Radojko/Shutterstock, (Kitten, Kangaroo, Duck) Getty Images, (Twins) John Foxx/Thinkstock, (Kick) Rubberball Productions, (Queen) Stockbyte/Thinkstock; **95** (Twins) John Foxx/Thinkstock, (King) Thinkstock; **96** (Twins) John Foxx/Thinkstock, (King) Thinkstock; **97** (Hot) ©Simone van den Berg/Alamy; **99** (Hot) ©Simone van den Berg/Alamy; **101** (Safety Pin) ©Ablestock/Index Open, (Can) Thinkstock; **103** (Safety Pin) ©Ablestock/Index Open, (Can) Thinkstock; **105** (Crab) Getty Images; **107** (Crab) Getty Images; **109** (Pup) ©Royalty-Free/Corbis, (Mop) Stockbyte/Thinkstock; **111** (Pup) ©Royalty-Free/Corbis, (Mop) Stockbyte/Thinkstock; **113** (Pig) ©Anat-oli/Shutterstock, (Bug) Brand X Pictures/Thinkstock; **115** (Pig) ©Anat-oli/Shutterstock, (Bug) Brand X Pictures/Thinkstock; **117** (Bell) Jupiter Images, (Mill) Photos to Go/Photolibrary; **119** (Bell) Jupiter Images, (Mill) Photos to Go/Photolibrary; **121** (Duck) Shutterstock; **123** (Duck) Shutterstock; **125** (Fish) ©Eric Isselée/Shutterstock, (Cash) Thinkstock; **127** (Fish) ©Eric Isselée/Shutterstock, (Cash) Thinkstock; **133** (Sink) ©Simple Stock Shots, (Trunk) Getty Images, (Tank) Shutterstock; **135** (Sink) ©Simple Stock Shots, (Trunk) Getty Images, (Tank) Shutterstock; **141** (Pig) ©Anat-oli/Shutterstock; **143** (Pig) ©Anat-oli/Shutterstock; **144** (Pig) ©Anat-oli/Shutterstock; **145** (Pig) ©Anat-oli/Shutterstock; **147** (Pig) ©Anat-oli/Shutterstock; **148** (Pig) ©Anat-oli/Shutterstock; **197** (Pig) ©Anat-oli/Shutterstock, (Kite) ©D. Hurst/Alamy, (Goat, Fish) ©Eric Isselée/Shutterstock, (Map) Digital Wisdom, Inc., (Saw) Getty Images, (Nest) Jupiter Images, (Jet) Photos to Go/Photolibrary, (Web, Ham) Thinkstock; **198** (Dad) ©Corbis, (Hat) ©Heath Doman/Shutterstock, (Hog) ©Tim Burrett/Shutterstock, (Bug) Brand X Pictures/Thinkstock, (Map) Digital Wisdom, Inc., (Cot) Hemera Technologies/Thinkstock, (Jet, Hill) Photos to Go/Photolibrary, (Mop) Stockbyte/Thinkstock, (Rip) Thinkstock; **199** (Tree) ©Borislav Gnjidic/Shutterstock, (Clouds) ©Royalty-Free/Corbis, (Frame) ©Valentin Agapov/Shutterstock, (Swim) Getty Images, (Twins) John Foxx/Thinkstock, (Snail) Jupiter Images, (Drill) Shutterstock, (Queen) Stockbyte/Thinkstock; **200** (Safety Pin) ©Ablestock/Index Open, (Pot) ©Margouillat Photo/Shutterstock, (Bat) Getty Images, (Mill) Photos to Go/Photolibrary, (Duck) Shutterstock, (Cash) Thinkstock; **201** (Fish) ©Eric Isselée/Shutterstock, (Fox) ©Jeremy Woodhouse/Getty Images, (Frog) ©Malcolm Schuyl/Alamy, (Crab) Getty Images, (Nest, Bell) Jupiter Images, (Can) Thinkstock; **202** (Swing) Getty Images, (Drink) Goodshoot/Jupiter Images, (Tent, Tank) Shutterstock, (Skunk, King) Thinkstock; **203** (Card) ©Aaron Amat/Shutterstock, (Car) ©Adisa/Shutterstock, (Cart) ©Andrey Armyagov/Shutterstock, (Goat) ©Eric Isselée/Shutterstock, (Thorn) ©Evgeni S./Shutterstock, (Shark) ©Prochasson Frederic/Shutterstock, (Crab) Getty Images, (Corn) Jupiter Images, (Yard) Photos to Go/Photolibrary, (Horn) Shutterstock.

ISBN-13: 978-1-4284-3131-7
ISBN-10:   1-4284-3131-4

23 17

Contents

Bb	Mm	Rr	Ss

Write a capital and lowercase b, m, r, and s on the lines. Then draw two pictures of things that begin with those letters.

Bb	Mm	Rr	Ss

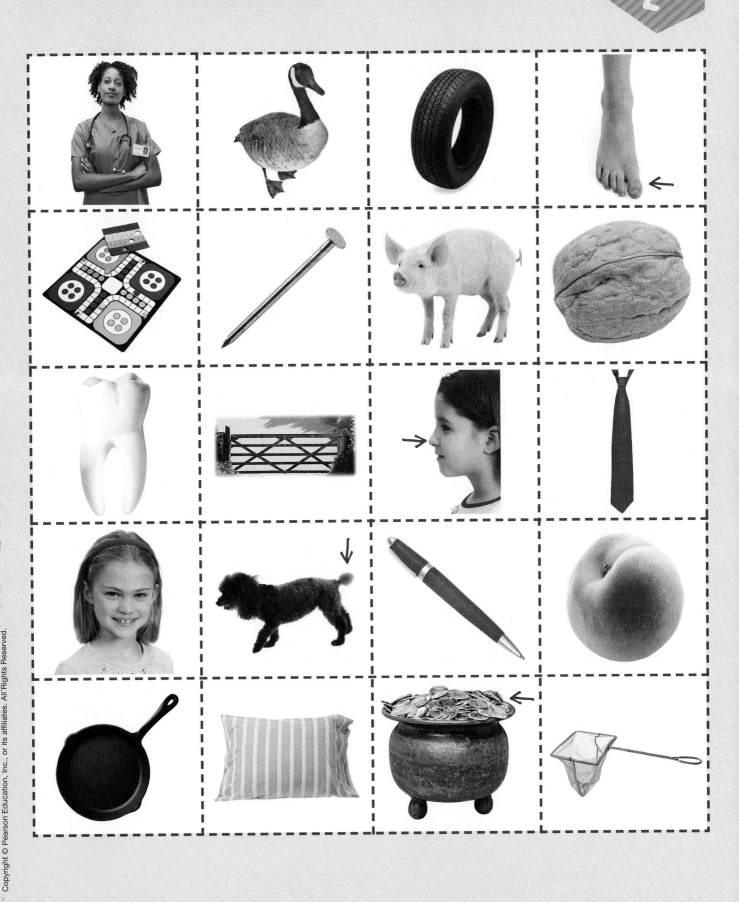

Tt	Gg	Nn	Pp

Write a capital and lowercase t, g, n, and p on the lines. Then draw two pictures of things that begin with those letters.

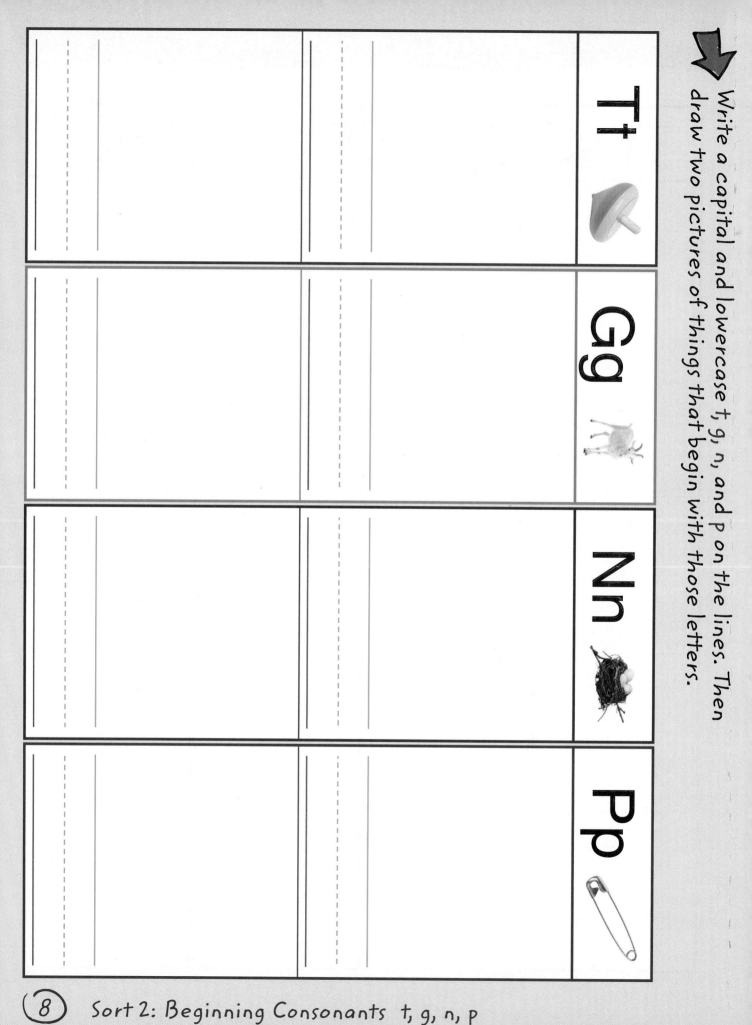

Tt	Gg	Nn	Pp

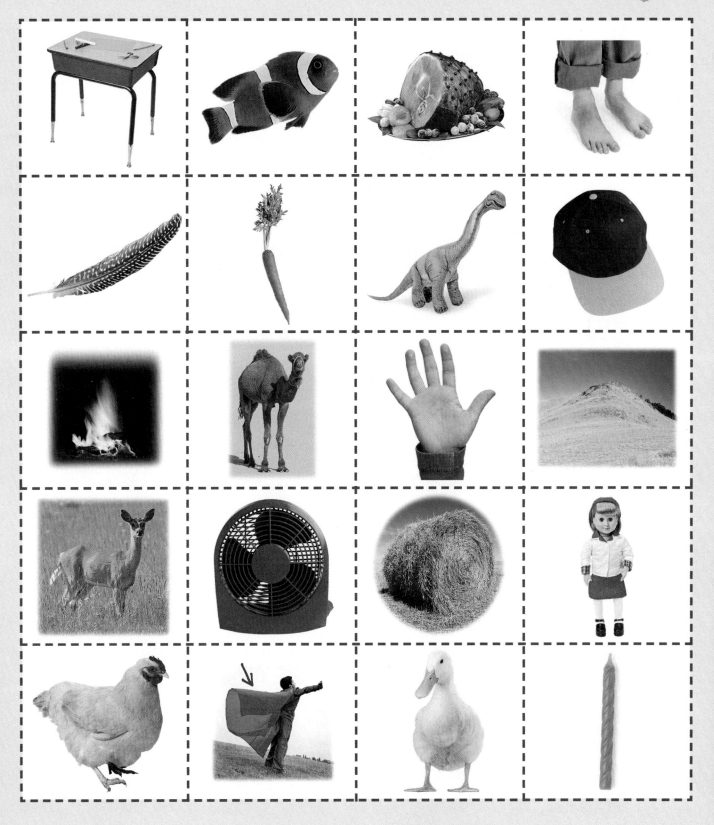

Cc	Hh	Ff	Dd

Write a capital and lowercase c, h, f, and d on the lines. Then draw two pictures of things that begin with those letters.

Cc

Hh

Ff

Dd

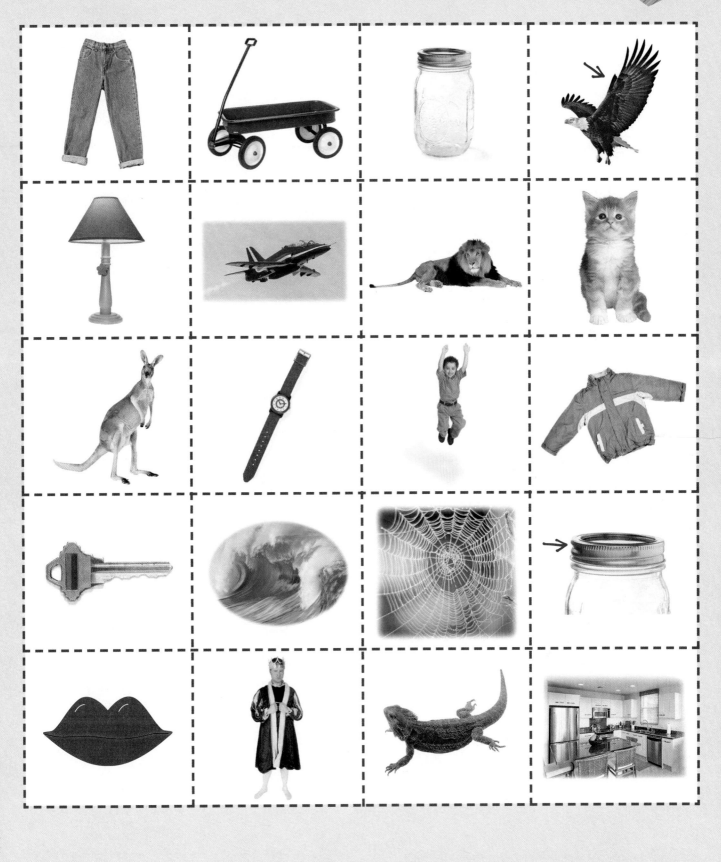

Ll	Kk	Jj	Ww

Write a capital and lowercase l, k, j, and w on the lines. Then draw two pictures of things that begin with those letters.

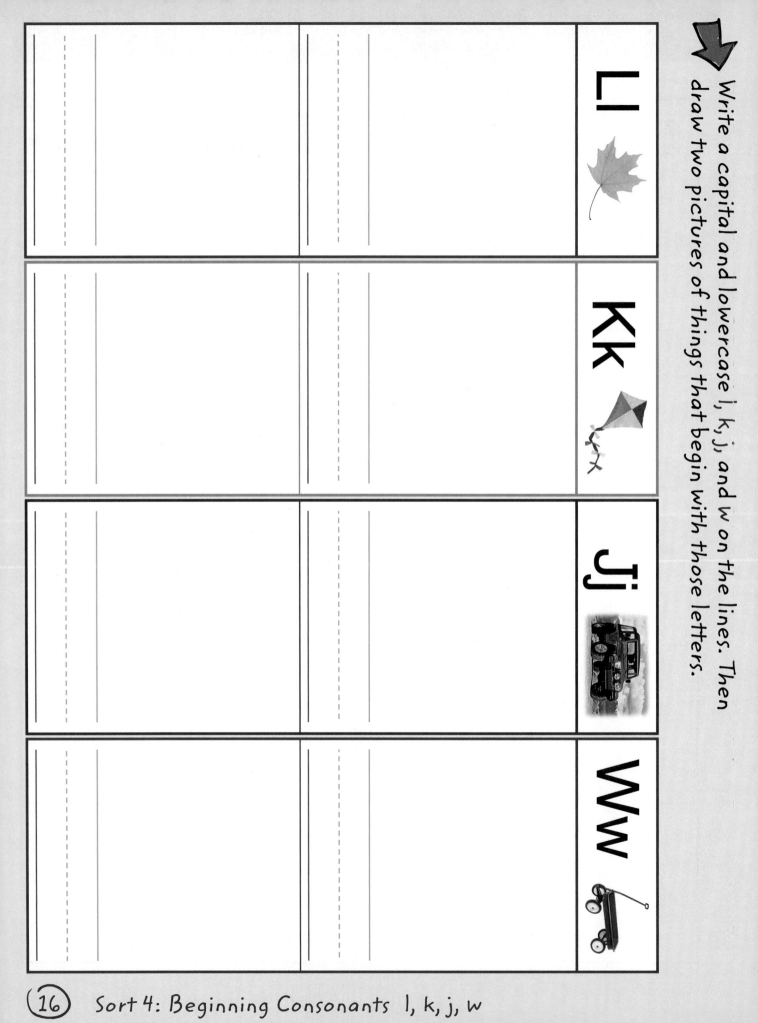

Ll

Kk

Jj

Ww

Yy 	Zz	Vv

Write a capital and lowercase y, z, and v on the lines. Then draw two pictures of things that begin with those letters.

Yy	Zz	Vv

Sort 5: Beginning Consonants y, z, v

Word Families -at, -an

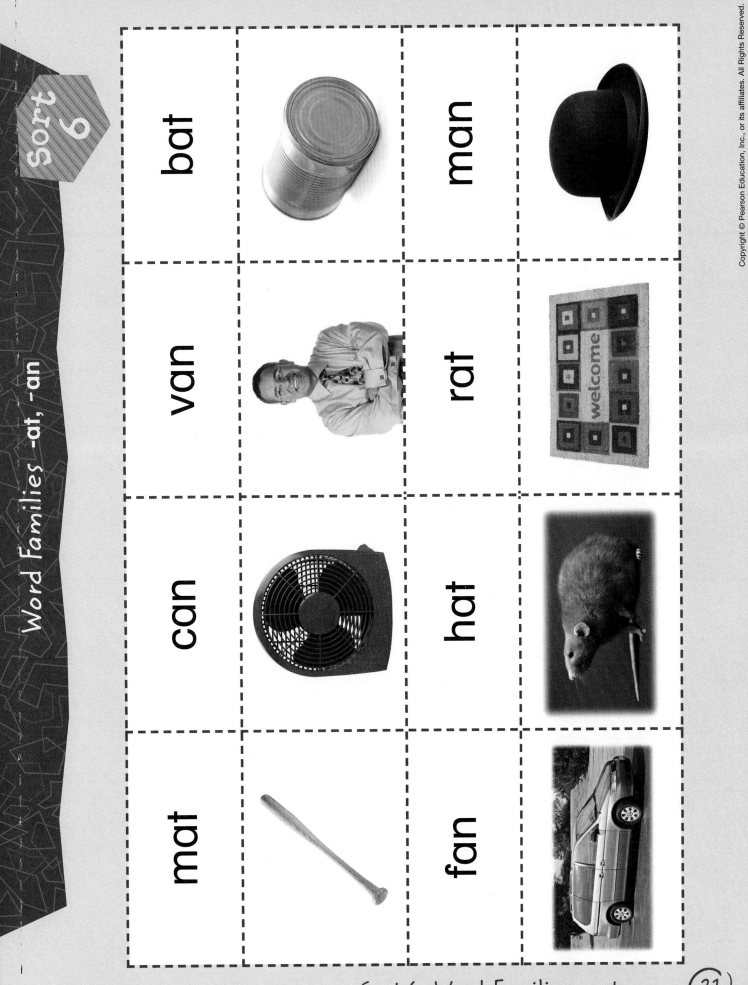

bat

man

van

rat

can

hat

mat

fan

-an

-at

Write on the lines words that rhyme with bat
and can.

bat	can

Sort 6: Word Families -at, -an

Word Families -ad, -an

man	sad	dad	fan

can	mad	van	pad

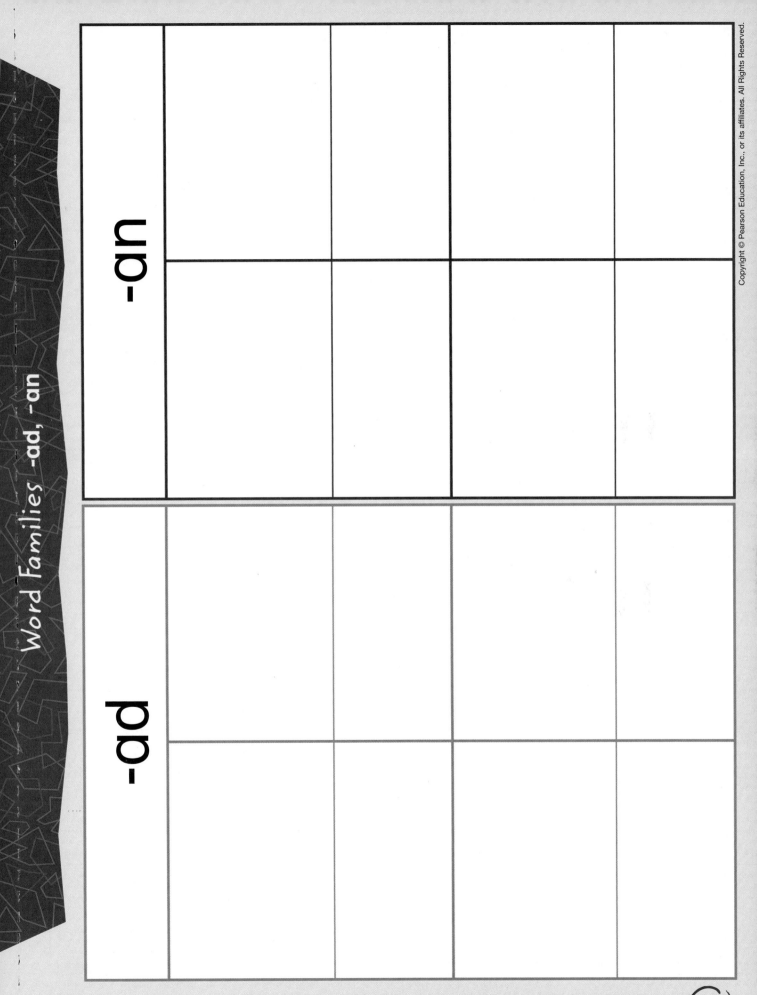

-an

-ad

Write on the lines words that rhyme with fan
and dad.

fan

dad

Sort 7: Word Families -ad, -an

-an

-ad

fan	dad

Word Families -ap, -ag

rag		lap	
cap		flag	
wag		tag	
nap		map	

Sort 8: Word Families -ap, -ag 29

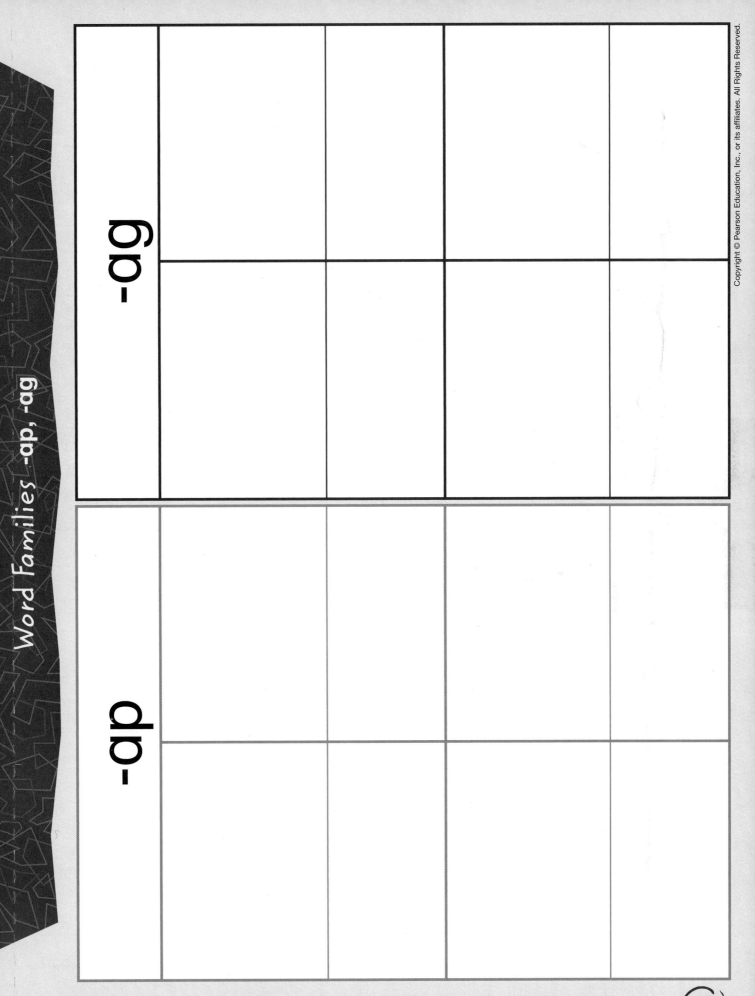

-ag

-ap

Sort 8: Word Families -ap, -ag (31)

Write on the lines words that rhyme with nap
and wag.

nap	wag

Sort 8: Word Families -ap, -ag

sad	nap	rag
cap	lap	dad
wag	pad	bag

-ad	-ap	-ag

sad

lap

bag

pot	hog	cot	hop
log	frog	top	jog
mop	dot	hot	pop

-og

-ot

-op

hop

hot

hog

zip	pig	wig
Jill	rip	sill
lip	mill	dig

-ip	-ig	-ill

lip

dig

mill

bug	nut	rug
run	sun	cut
mug	bun	hut

-ug	-ut	-un

rug

hut

run

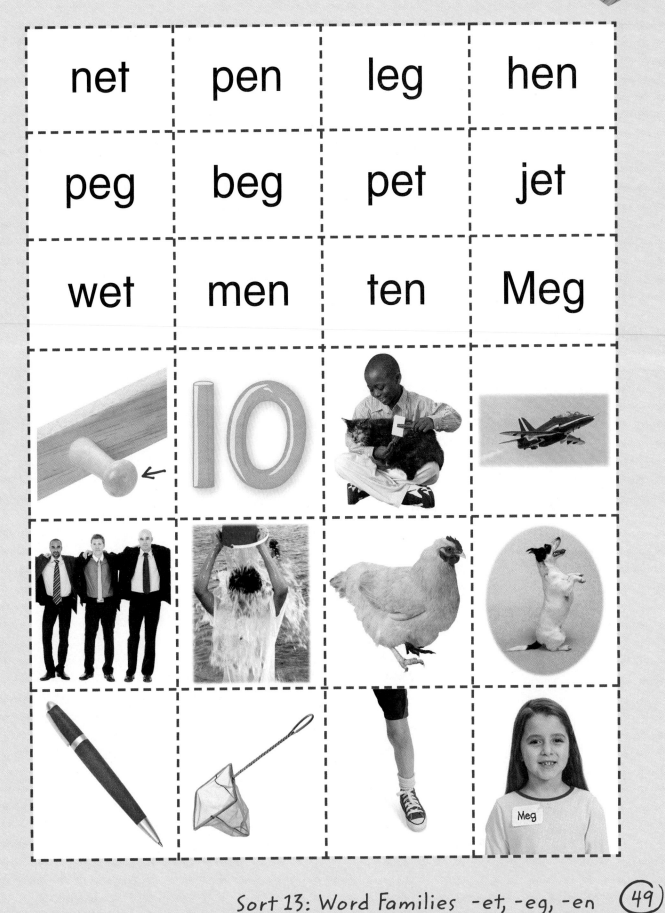

net	pen	leg	hen
peg	beg	pet	jet
wet	men	ten	Meg

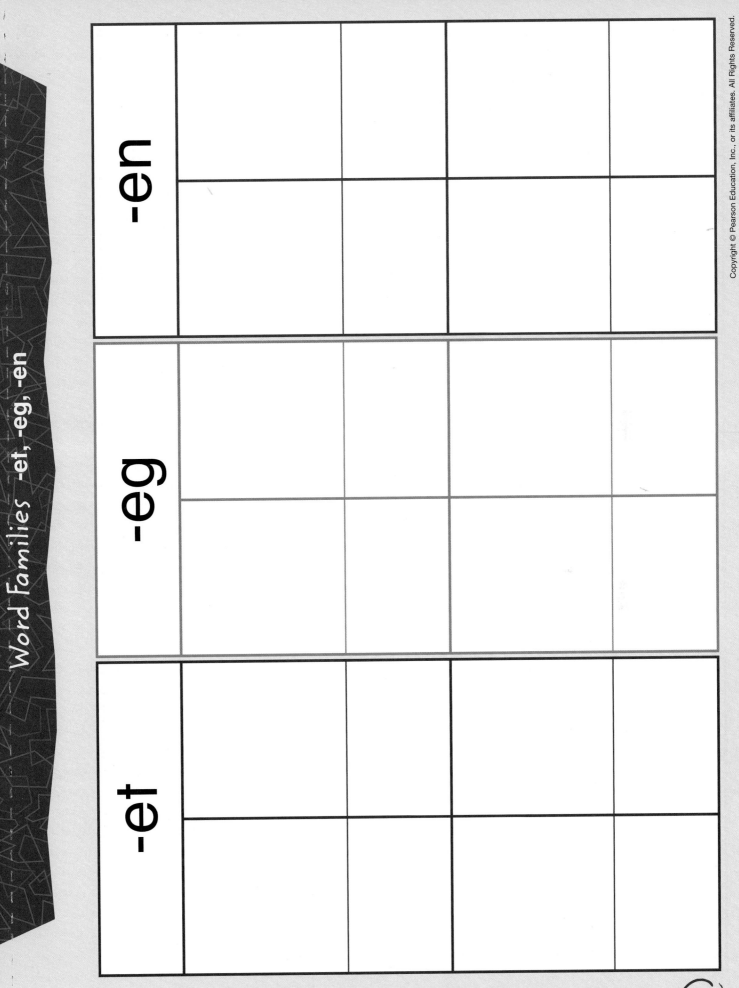

-en

-eg

-et

net

peg

pen

Word Families -ed, -et, -eg, -ell

-ed	-et	-eg	-ell
beg	sled	leg	sell
wet	tell	Meg	shell
led	peg	met	wed
bet	get	fell	red
set	bell	bed	

-ell					

-eg					

-et					

-ed					

Sort 14: Word Families -ed, -et, -eg, -ell (55)

Write on the lines words that rhyme with bed, met, leg, and bell.

bed	met	leg	bell

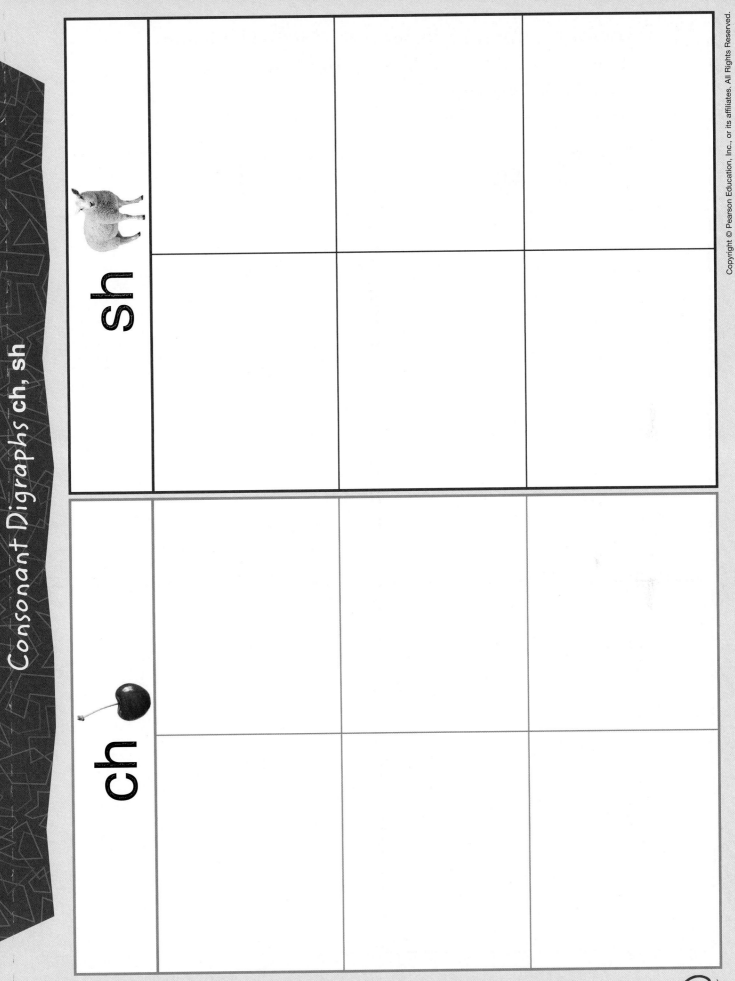

Sort 15: Consonant Digraphs ch, sh (59)

Draw two pictures of things that start with ch and two things that start with sh. Write ch and sh below the matching pictures.

ch

sh

Sort 15: Consonant Digraphs ch, sh

wh

th

Draw two pictures of things that start with wh and two things that start with th. Write wh and th below the matching pictures.

th 👍	wh ⚙

sh	ch	wh	th

sh	ch	wh	th

Sort 17: Consonant Digraphs sh, ch, wh, th

Sort 18: Beginning Consonants and Blends s, t, st (69)

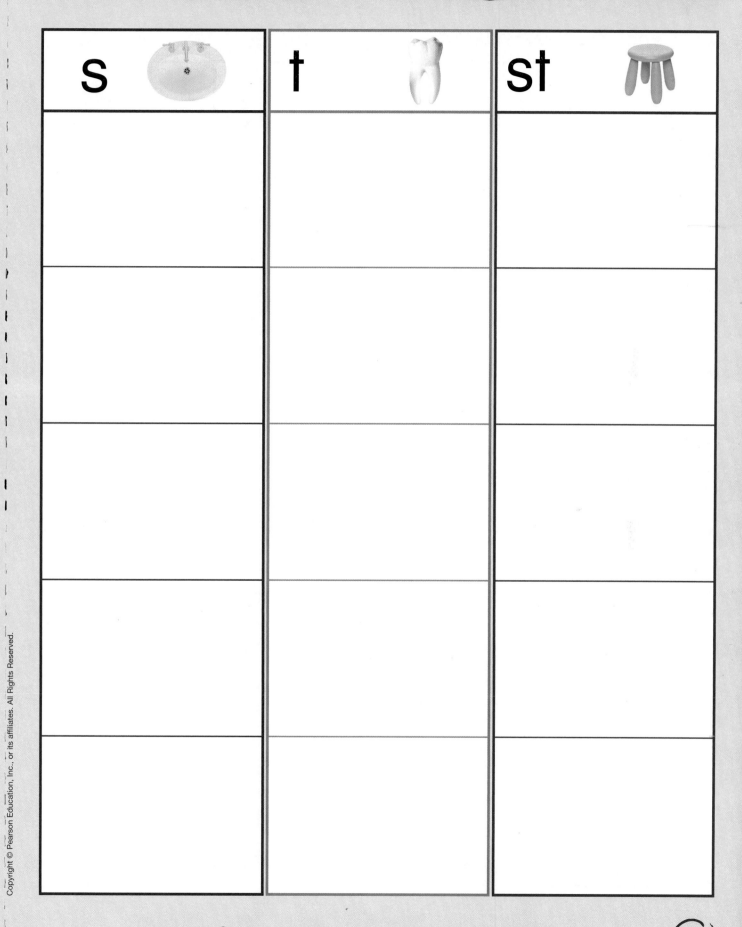

s	t	st

Draw two pictures of things that start with s, t, and st. Write the beginning sound below each picture.

Sort 18: Beginning Consonants and Blends s, t, st

sp	sk	sm

Sort 19: Consonant Blends sp, sk, sm   75

Draw two pictures of things that start with sp, sk, and sm. Write the beginning sound below each picture.

sp	sk	sm

Sort 19: Consonant Blends sp, sk, sm

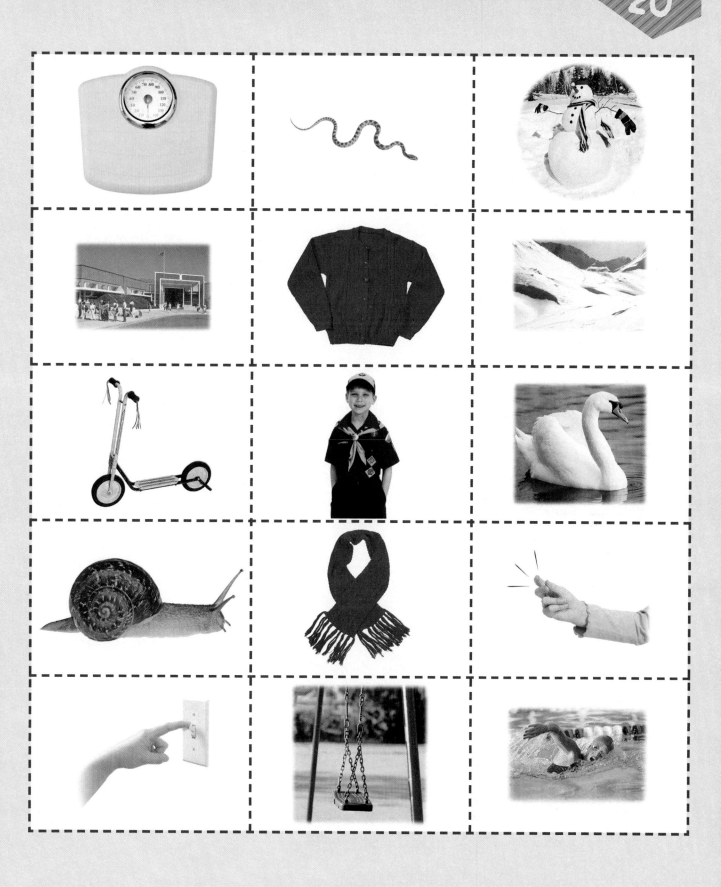

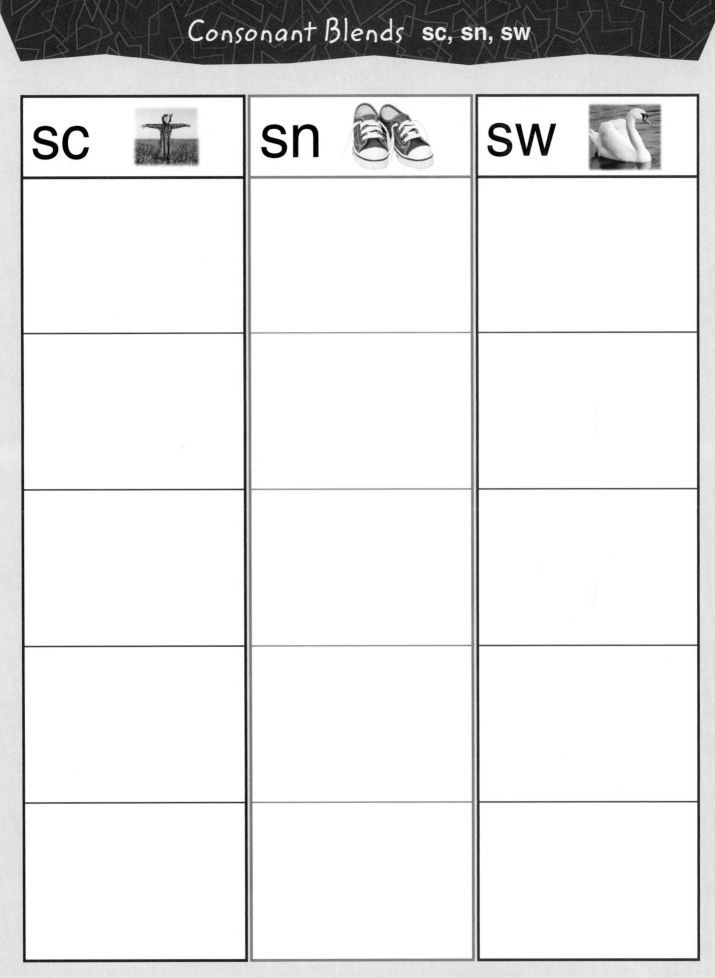

sc	sn	sw

Draw two pictures of things that start with sc, sn, and sw. Write the beginning sound below each picture.

sc	sn	sw

Sort 20: Consonant Blends sc, sn, sw

pl	sl	bl	fl

Draw two pictures of things that start with pl, sl, bl, and fl.
Write the beginning sound below each picture.

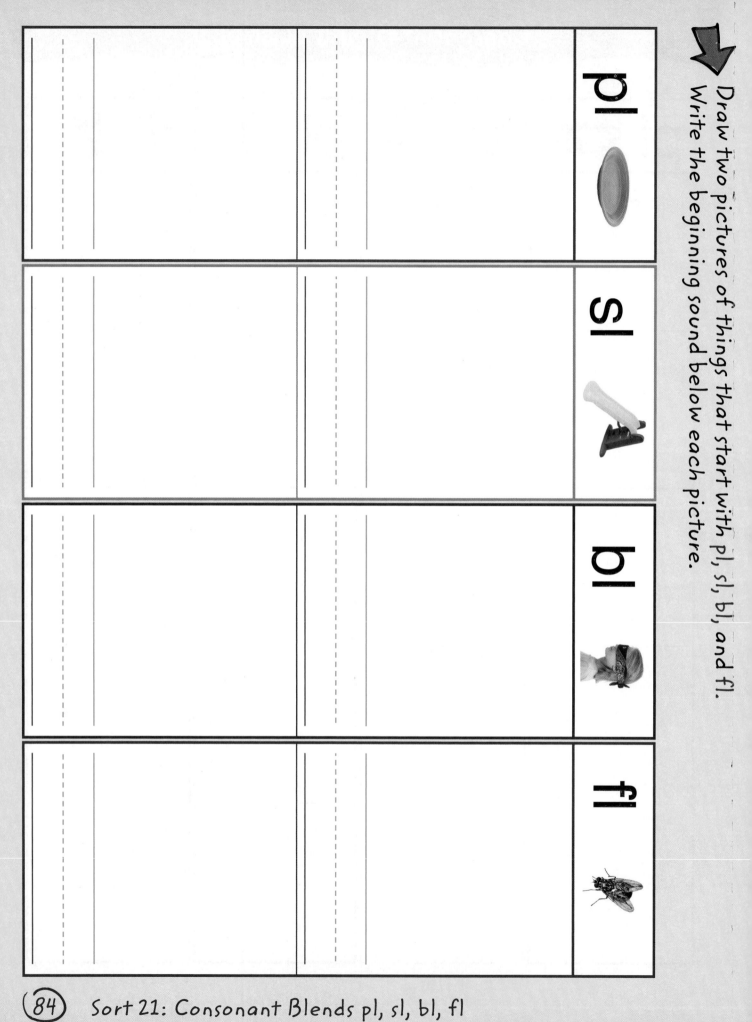

| pl | sl | bl | fl |

Sort 21: Consonant Blends pl, sl, bl, fl

Consonant Blends cr, cl, fr, gl, gr

Sort 22: Consonant Blends cr, cl, fr, gl, gr   85

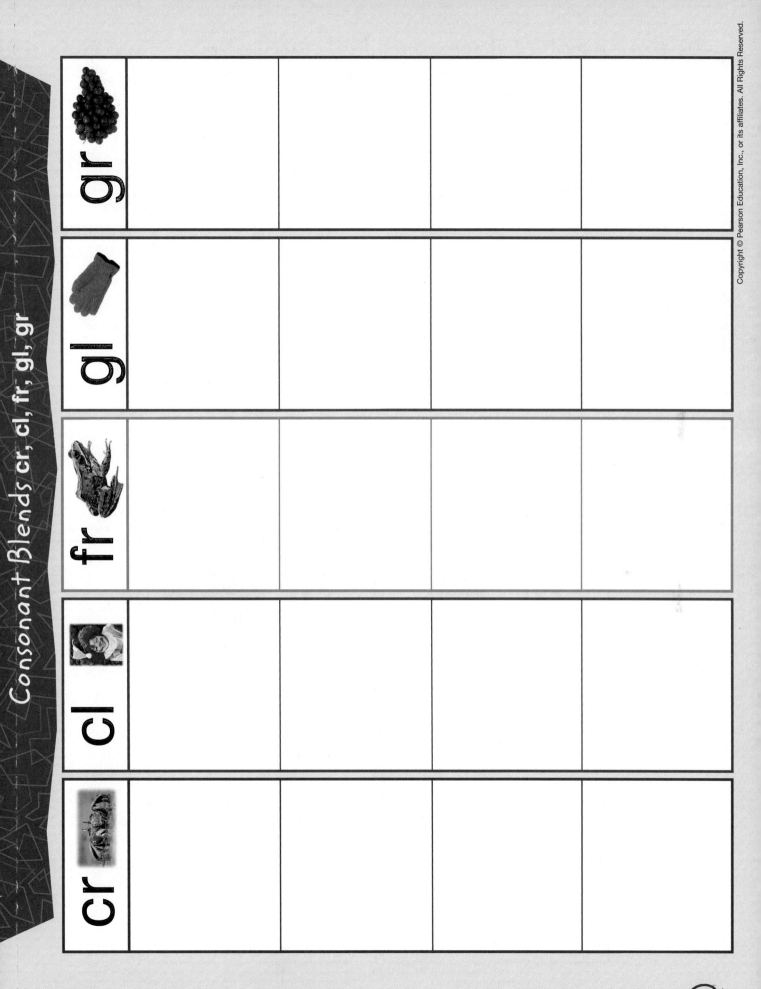

Consonant Blends cr, cl, fr, gl, gr

gr				
gl				
fr				
cl				
cr				

Draw a picture of something that starts with cr, cl, fr, gl, and gr. Write the beginning sound below each picture.

cr	cl	fr

gl	gr

pr	tr	dr	br

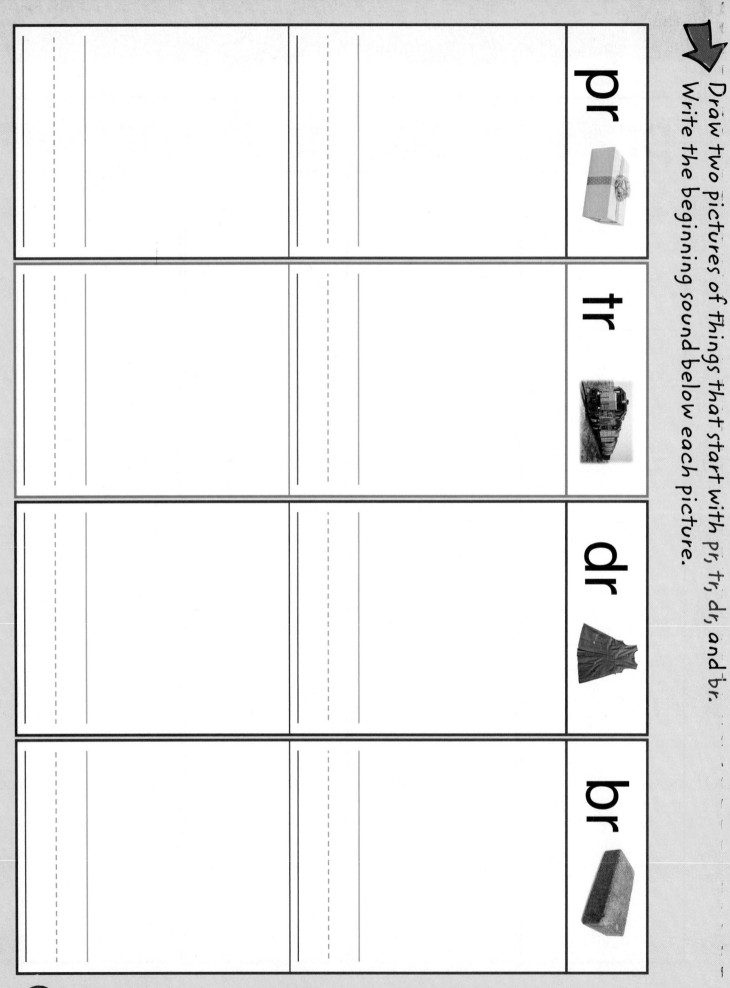

pr	tr	dr	br

k	wh	qu	tw

k 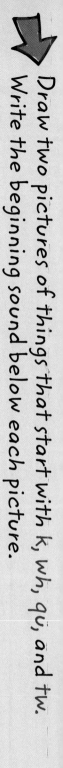	wh	qu	tw

cat	hot	sit
not	fit	that
bat	cot	dot
got	fat	bit
hit	mat	slot
spot	kit	flat
rat	lit	trot
pit	chat	quit

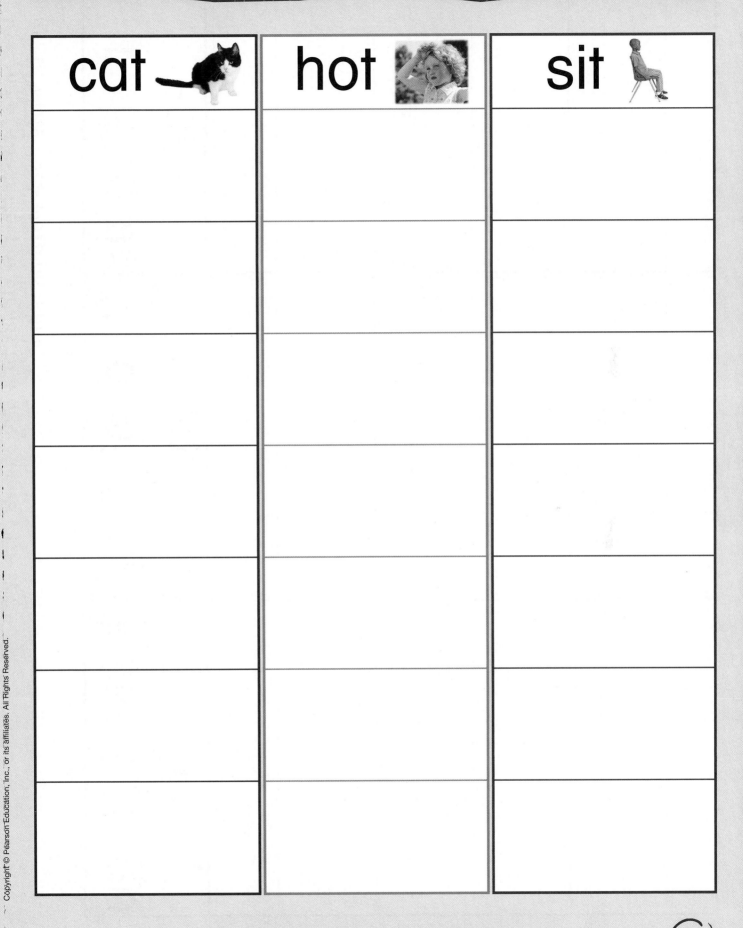

cat	hot	sit

b r fl m th	-at

tr d sl c sp	-ot

h k l b qu	-it

sun	ten 10	pin	can
skin	fan	bun	thin
win	pen	man	then
run	chin	ran	plan
pan	grin	fun	hen
than	men	fin	when

Sort 26: Mixed Vowel Word Families -an, -in, -en, -un (101)

sun ✳						
ten 10						
pin						
can						

f m pl th r	-an

ch gr w f	-in

wh m m th h	-en

r f b	-un

Mixed Vowel Word Families -ad, -ed, -ab, -ob

cob	crab	bed	sad
tab	mad	rob	red
had	mob	fed	blob
lab	sob	bad	led
glad	glob	shed	pad
cab	sled	grab	job

Sort 27: Mixed Vowel Word Families -ad, -ed, -ab, -ob (105)

cob	crab	bed	sad

Sort 27: Mixed Vowel Word Families -ad, -ed, -ab, -ob (107)

m gl b h	-ad

sh r sl f	-ed

gr c l t	-ab

r s gl j	-ob

Mixed Vowel Word Families -ap, -ip, -op, -up

cap	zip	mop	pup
flip	cup	whip	snap
top	clap	hop	zap
chop	hip	crop	tap
pop	up	dip	lap
trip	drop	ship	trap

Sort 28: Mixed Vowel Word Families -ap, -ip, -op, -up

pup	mop	zip	cap

Sort 28: Mixed Vowel Word Families -ap, -ip, -op, -up   (111)

sn z l tr	-ap

d h tr fl	-ip

t h p dr	-op

c p	-up

Sort 28: Mixed Vowel Word Families -ap, -ip, -op, -up

Mixed Vowel Word Families -ag, -eg, -ig, -og, -ug

tag	leg	pig	dog	bug
rag	hug	bag	log	rug
wag	fig	peg	big	wig
jog	Meg	flag	frog	drug
slug	plug	snag	beg	hog
dig	fog	twig	mug	jig

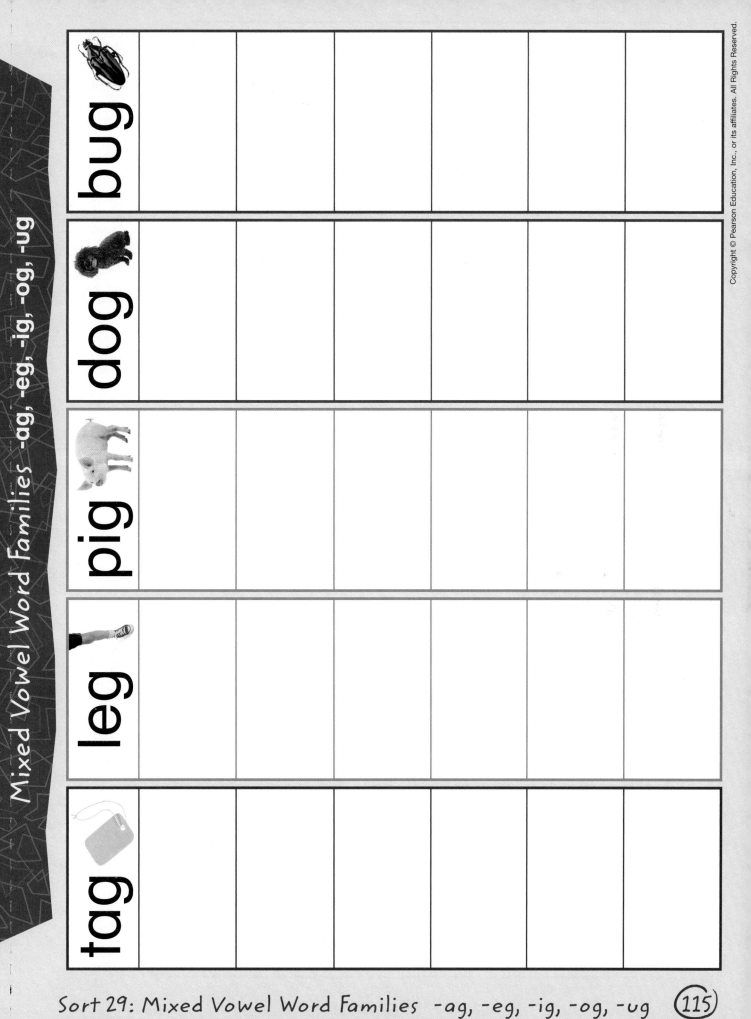

Mixed Vowel Word Families -ag, -eg, -ig, -og, -ug

bug

dog

pig

leg

tag

Sort 29: Mixed Vowel Word Families -ag, -eg, -ig, -og, -ug   (115)

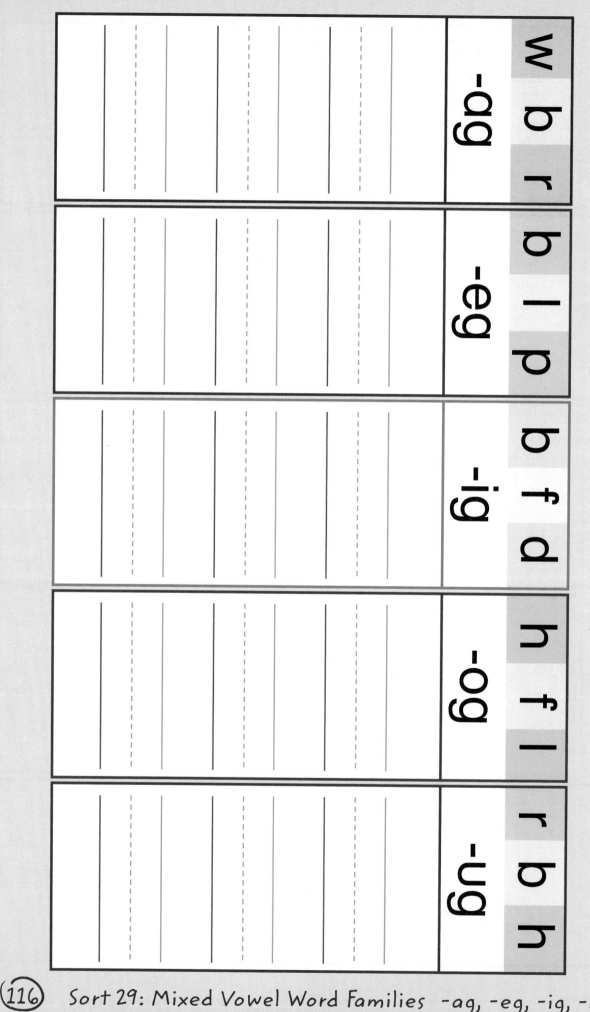

w b r	b l p	b f d	h f l	r b h
-ag	-eg	-ig	-og	-ug

mill	bell	ball
fell	bill	hall
will	fall	mall
fill	call	chill
well	tall	shell
small	smell	spill
sell	hill	tell

mill 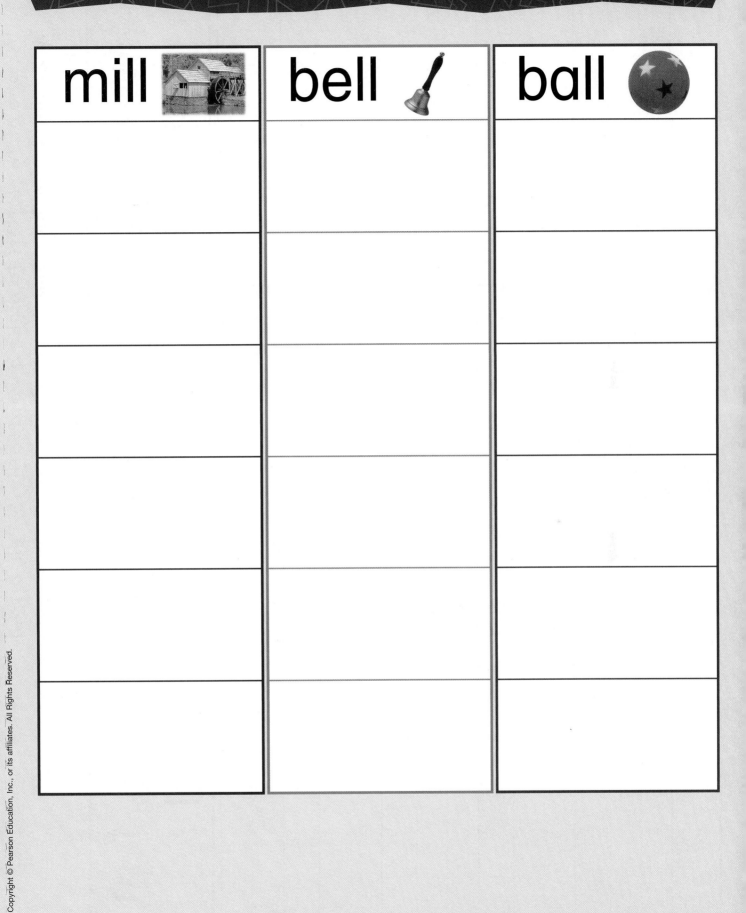	bell	ball

f w h m ch	f t s w sh	b c h f t
-ill	-ell	-all

sack	brick	lock	duck
truck	pack	stuck	trick
tuck	back	clock	thick
rock	kick	pluck	black
luck	chick	flock	lick
rack	tack	dock	block

Sort 31: Mixed Vowel Word Families -ack, -ick, -ock, -uck (121)

duck	lock	brick	sack

Sort 31: Mixed Vowel Word Families -ack, -ick, -ock, -uck (123)

l k ch th	p r bl t	tr l st d	r l d cl
-ick	-ack	-uck	-ock

fish	cash	brush
rush	dash	wish
flash	swish	crush
fish	mush	blush
crash	flush	smash
hush	rash	dish
trash	mash	plush

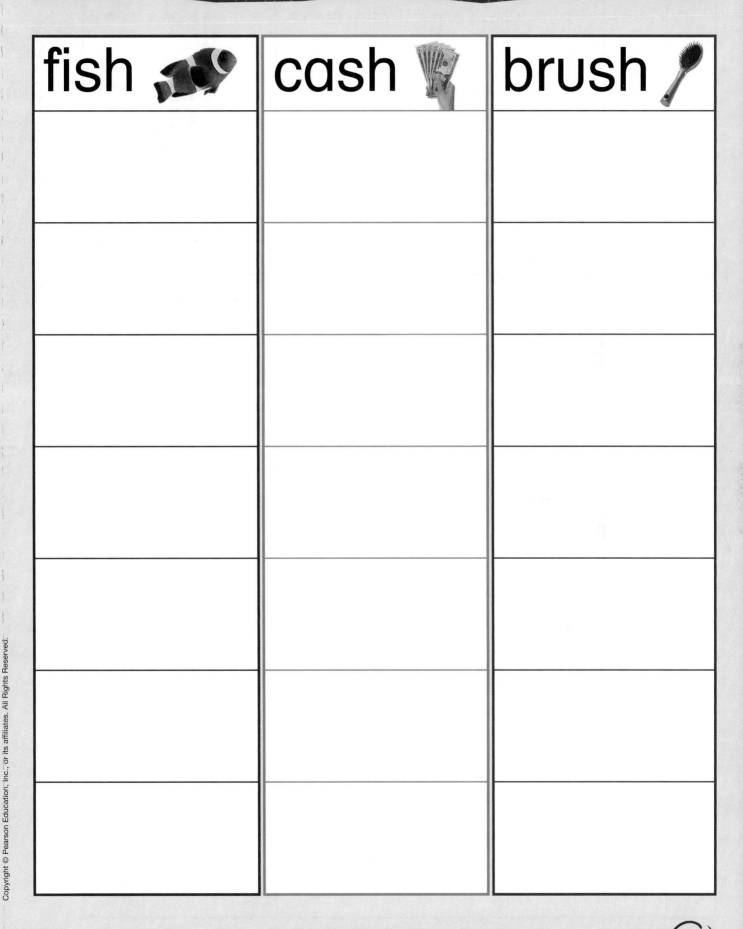

fish	cash	brush

w d sw f	-ish

m r cr d sm	-ash

br r h m cr	-ush

Sort 32: Mixed Vowel Word Families -ash, -ish, -ush

Mixed Vowel Word Families -ang, -ing, -ong, -ung

-ang	-ing	-ong	-ung
strong	sung	ring	sang
bring	gang	gong	stung
king	rang	clang	long
ding	rung	hang	lung
sting	sing	song	fang

Mixed Vowel Word Families -ang, -ing, -ong, -ung

-ung						

-ong						

-ing						

-ang						

Sort 33: Mixed Vowel Word Families -ang, -ing, -ong, -ung   (131)

s	h	cl	r	-ang

r	d	s	k	br	-ing

s	l	g	str	-ong

l	s	r	st	-ung

tank	sink	trunk
bunk	junk	sank
chunk	bank	think
drink	ink	sunk
skunk	thank	link
plank	hunk	blink
prank	blank	stink
dunk	yank	wink

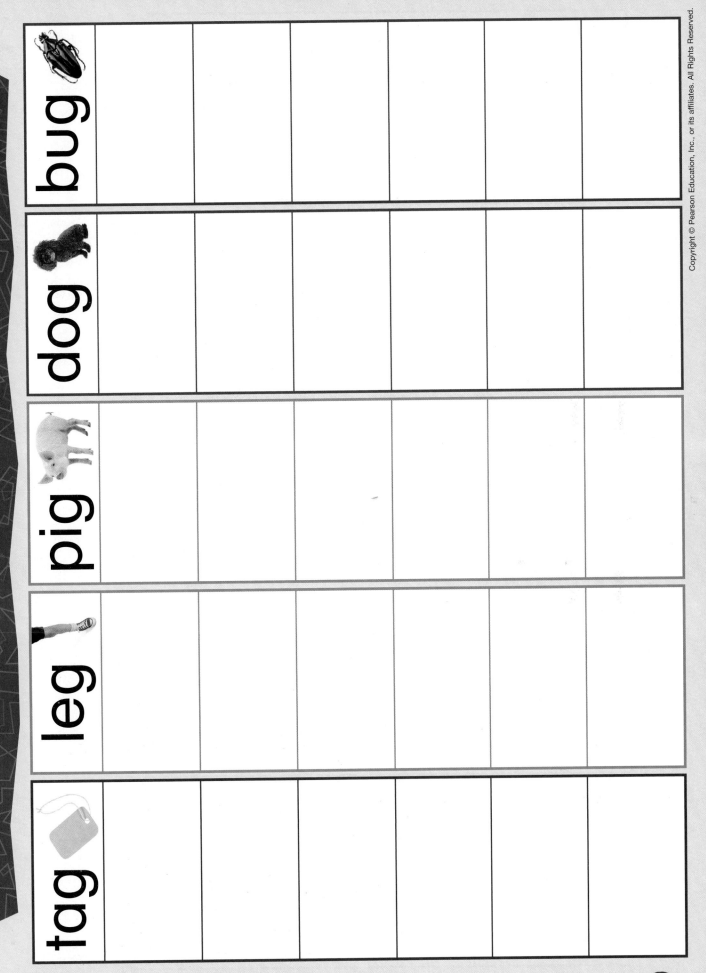

Sort 29: Mixed Vowel Word Families -ag, -eg, -ig, -og, -ug (115)

Use one of the letters to make a word with -ag, -eg, -ig, -og, or -ug. Write each word on a line.

w b r	-ag	

b l p	-eg	

b f d	-ig	

h f l	-og	

r b h	-ug	

Sort 29: Mixed Vowel Word Families -ag, -eg, -ig, -og, -ug

mill	bell	ball
fell	bill	hall
will	fall	mall
fill	call	chill
well	tall	shell
small	smell	spill
sell	hill	tell

mill	bell	ball

f w h m ch	-ill
f t s w sh	-ell
b c h f t	-all

sack	brick	lock	duck
truck	pack	stuck	trick
tuck	back	clock	thick
rock	kick	pluck	black
luck	chick	flock	lick
rack	tack	dock	block

duck	lock	brick	sack

Sort 31: Mixed Vowel Word Families -ack, -ick, -ock, -uck

l k ch th	-ick	

p r bl t	-ack	

tr l st d	-uck	

r l d cl	-ock	

fish	cash	brush
rush	dash	wish
flash	swish	crush
fish	mush	blush
crash	flush	smash
hush	rash	dish
trash	mash	plush

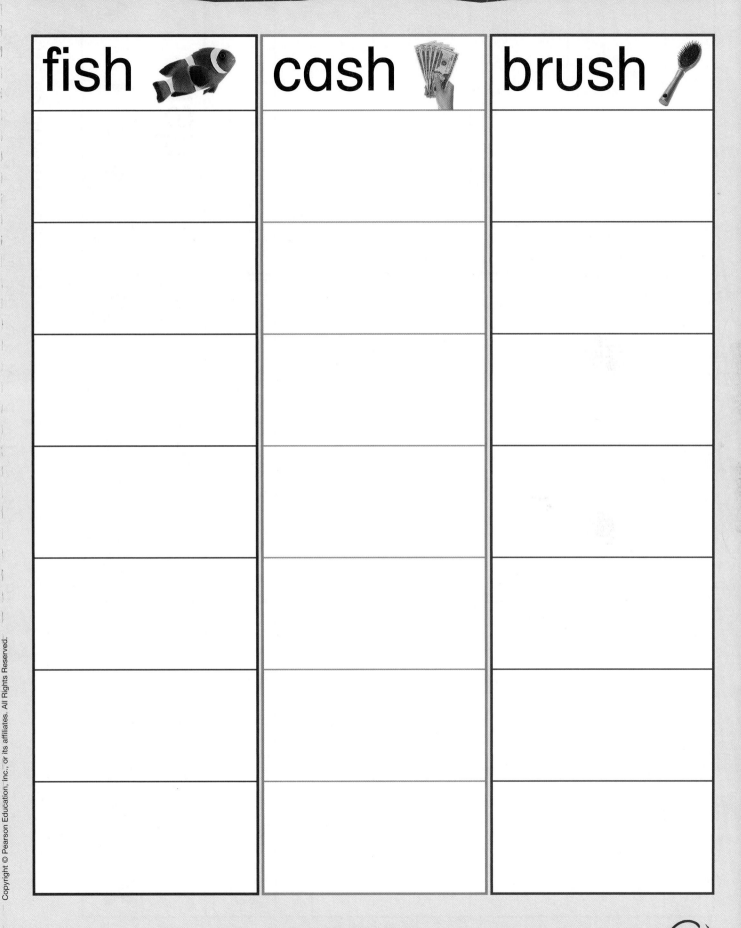

fish	cash	brush

w d sw f	-ish
m r cr d sm br	-ash
r h m cr	-ush

-ang	-ing	-ong	-ung
strong	sung	ring	sang
bring	gang	gong	stung
king	rang	clang	long
ding	rung	hang	lung
sting	sing	song	fang

-ung						

-ong						

-ing						

-ang						

Mixed Vowel Word Families -ang, -ing, -ong, -ung

Sort 33: Mixed Vowel Word Families -ang, -ing, -ong, -ung (131)

s	h	cl	r		-ang

d	s	k	br		-ing

s	l	g	str		-ong

l	s	r	st		-ung

tank	sink	trunk
bunk	junk	sank
chunk	bank	think
drink	ink	sunk
skunk	thank	link
plank	hunk	blink
prank	blank	stink
dunk	yank	wink

tank	sink	trunk

s th bl y r	-ank

l st dr w bl	-ink

ch h b j s	-unk

cat	sock	oddball	wag	ran
top	hop	had	was	for
ham	box	lot	cab	bag
mop	hot	mom	sad	jam
fox	got	map		
job				

Short Vowels a, o

oddball

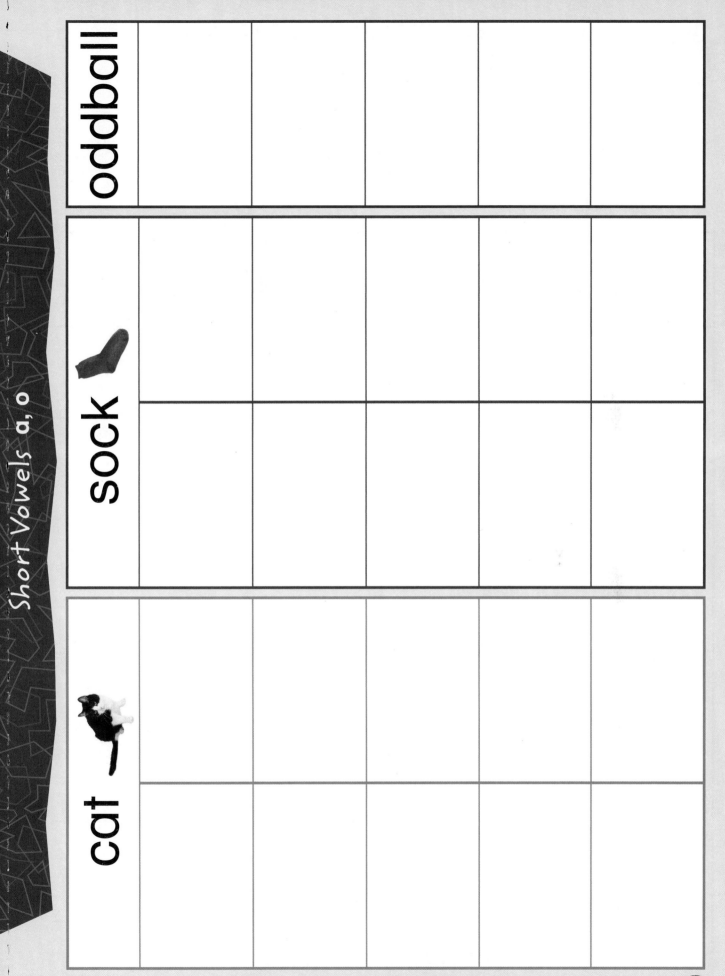

sock

cat

Say each word in the box. Print each word under the key word that has the same short vowel sound.

sad	bag	fox	hop
mom	job	ran	lot
got	cab	jam	wag

cat

sock

Short Vowels i, u

pig	cup	oddball		
zip	jug	will	rub	rip
big	tub	cut	run	fun
win	him	hum	nut	gum
did	put	six	bit	pin
but				

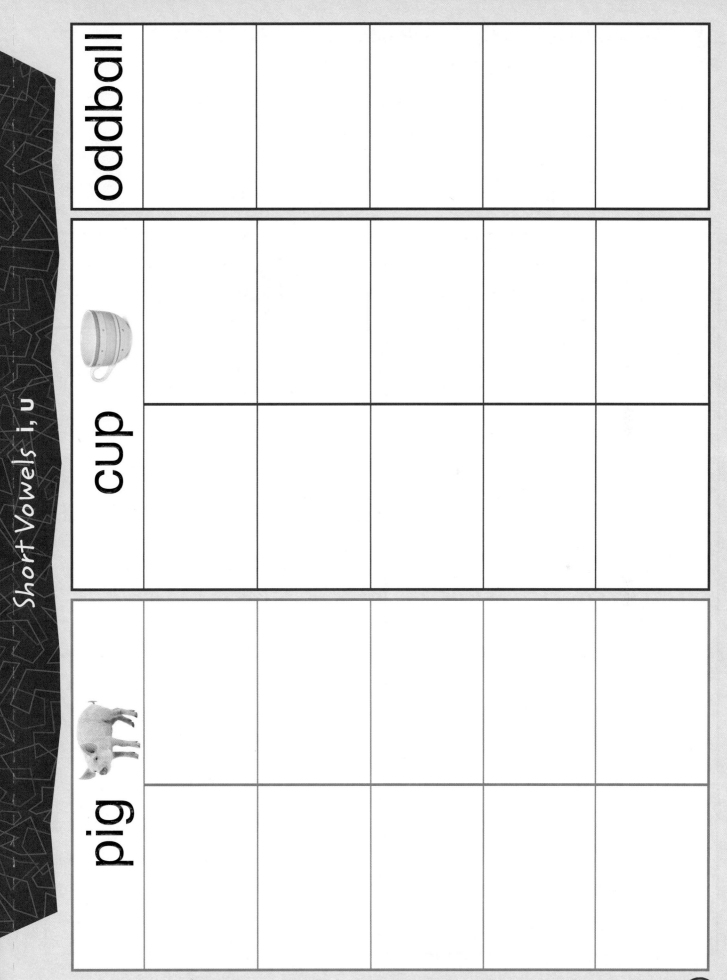

oddball				

cup

pig

Say each word in the box. Print each word under the key word that has the same short vowel sound.

six	gum	pin	bit
hum	fun	tub	cut
did	zip	nut	will

pig

cup

bed	pig	sock	cup
wet	six	pop	not
pet	miss	his	mud
mix	yes	hid	hot
let	bus	cub	bug
sun	bell		

cup					

sock					

pig					

bed					

Sort 37: Short Vowels e, i, o, u (147)

bed	pig	sock	cup

hid	cub	hot	six
wet	sun	bell	pop
his	not	mud	den

Short a, i Words With Beginning Blends

ă	ĭ			
drill	brag	flag	slip	glad
clap	grip	flat	plan	clip
drip	flip	crab	grab	cram
slap	brat	trap	slid	drag
		grill	skip	spin

Sort 38: Short a, i Words With Beginning Blends (149)

i

a

Say each word in the box. Print each word under the box that shows its short vowel sound.

glad	flip	slap	slip
brag	flag	clip	grill
drip	slid	flat	trap

ă

ĭ

Sort 38: Short a, i Words With Beginning Blends

ĕ	ŏ	ŭ
trot	club	sled
fret	plot	drop
bled	slug	plum
dress	cross	drum
plug	frog	drug
slob	truck	slot

ĕ	ŏ	ŭ

Draw two pictures of things with the short vowel sounds of e, o, and u. Write the word below each picture.

ĕ	ŏ	ŭ

Sort 39: Short e, o, u Words With Beginning Blends

that	chat	thick
them	than	chap
shed	then	thin
whip	shack	wham
chill	ship	chest
shell	check	when
chick	whiz	shall

sock			fork		oddball

Say each word in the box. Print each word under the key word that has the same vowel sound.

fox	for	born	spot
sport	pond	sort	torn
shop	rot	drop	storm

sock

fork

Short a and ar

cat 	star ⭐	oddball	
car	far	drag	crab
farm	rag	snap	bark
crash	art	war	card
trap	yard	flag	dark
shark	brag	grand	jar

oddball				

star ⭐				

cat 🐱				

Say each word in the box. Print each word under the key word that has the same vowel sound.

farm	bark	brag	car
snap	crash	jar	trap
card	crab	dark	drag

cat

start

Sort 48: Short a and ar

that's	he is	was not
do not	here's	can not
didn't	does not	that is
who is	what is	don't
can't	he's	who's
doesn't	here is	did not
what's	wasn't	

isn't	is not	it's	it is

Say each contraction. Print each contraction under the word that is part of the contraction.

| didn't | that's | don't | here's | can't |
| wasn't | who's | he's | doesn't | what's |

is

not

Sort 49: Contractions

Say the name of each picture. Write the capital and lowercase letter that stands for the beginning sound.

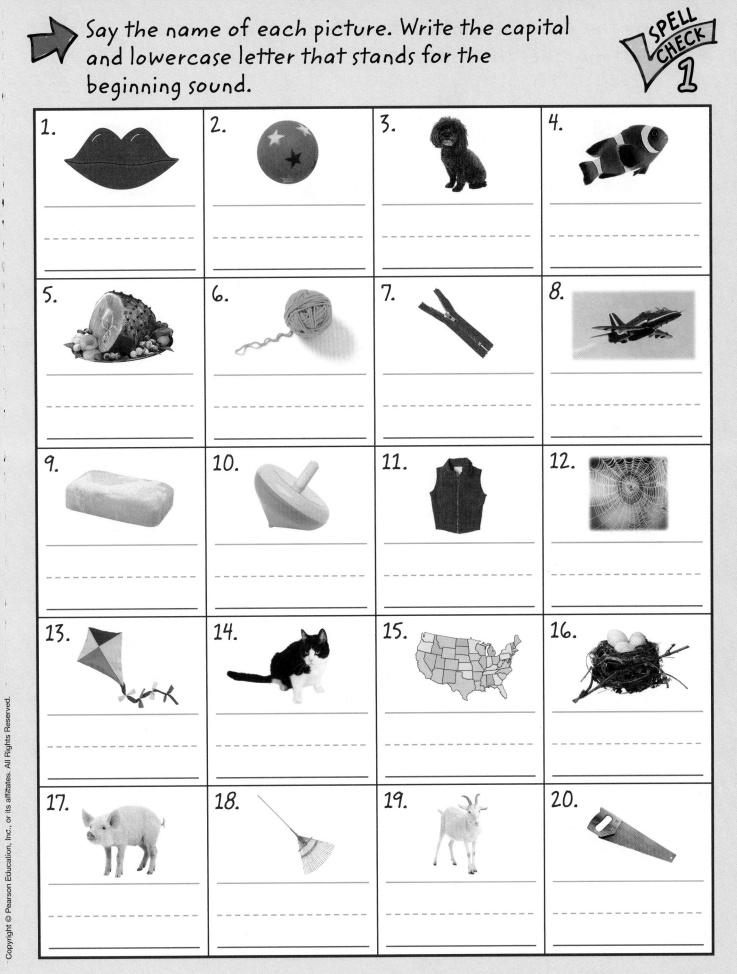

1.

2.

3.

4.

5.

6.

7.

8.

9.

10.

11.

12.

13.

14.

15.

16.

17.

18.

19.

20.

Spell Check 1: Beginning Consonants   197

Say the name of each picture. Circle the word that matches the picture.

SPELL CHECK 2

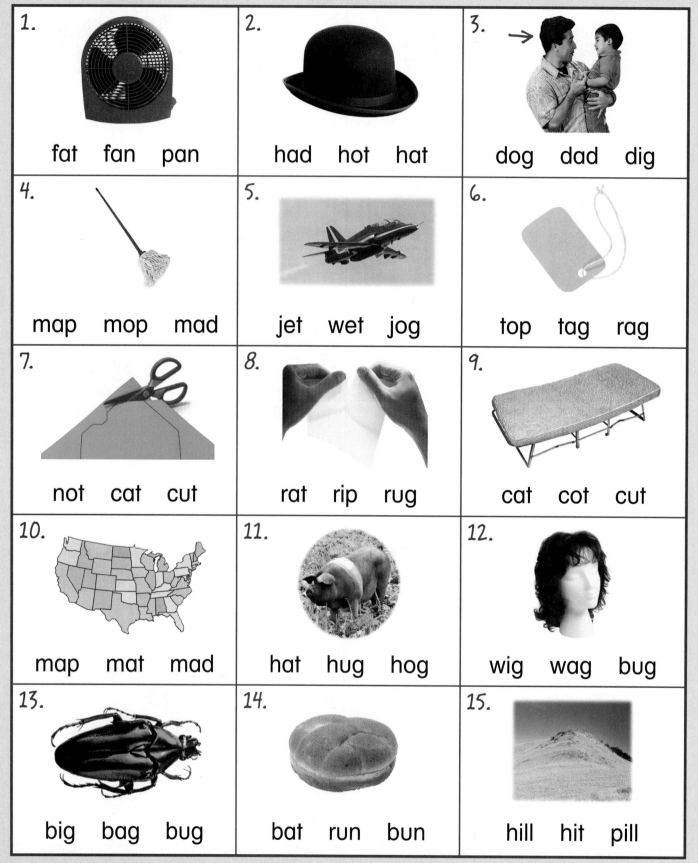

1. fat   fan   pan

2. had   hot   hat

3. dog   dad   dig

4. map   mop   mad

5. jet   wet   jog

6. top   tag   rag

7. not   cat   cut

8. rat   rip   rug

9. cat   cot   cut

10. map   mat   mad

11. hat   hug   hog

12. wig   wag   bug

13. big   bag   bug

14. bat   run   bun

15. hill   hit   pill

1.

2.

3.

4.

5.

6.

7.

8.

9.

10.

11.

12.

13.

14.

15.

16.

17.

18.

19.

20.

Think about the vowel sound you hear in the name of each picture. Write the word on the line below the picture.

SPELL CHECK 4

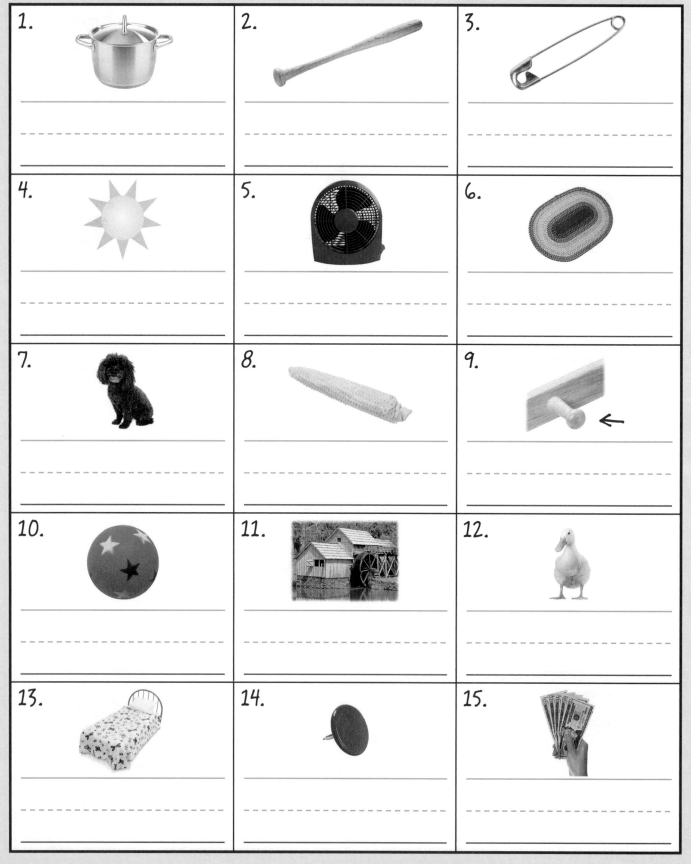

1.

2.

3.

4.

5.

6.

7.

8.

9.

10.

11.

12.

13.

14.

15.

200 Spell Check 4: Mixed Vowel Word Families

Write the picture names on the lines.

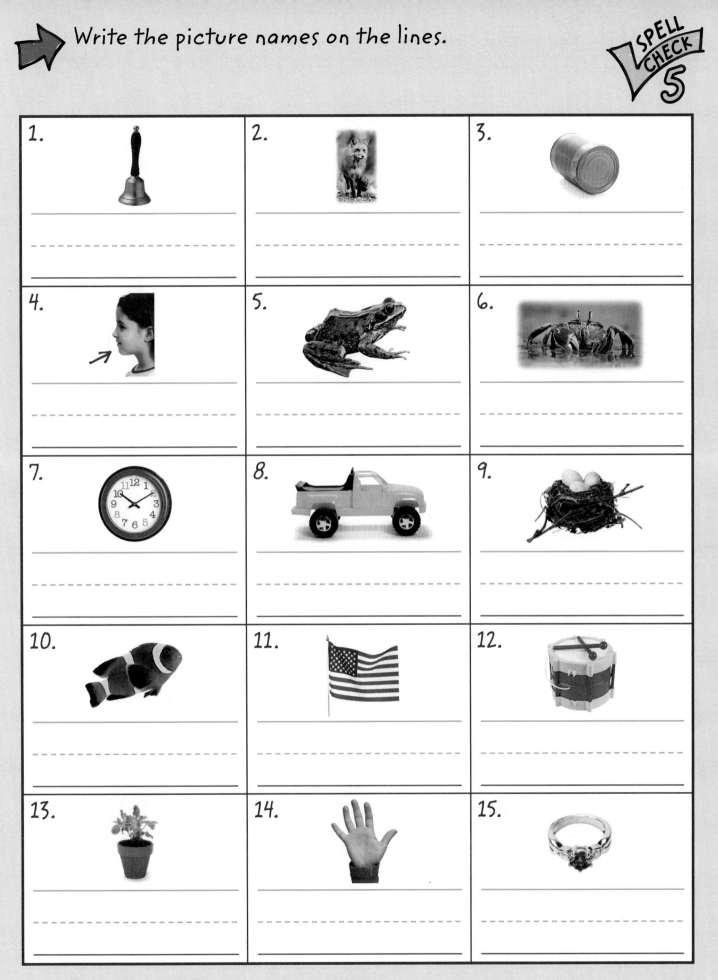

1.

2.

3.

4.

5.

6.

7.

8.

9.

10.

11.

12.

13.

14.

15.

Write the picture names on the lines.

1.

2.

3.

4.

5.

6.

7.

8.

9.

10.

11.

12.

Spell Check 6: Preconsonantal Nasals

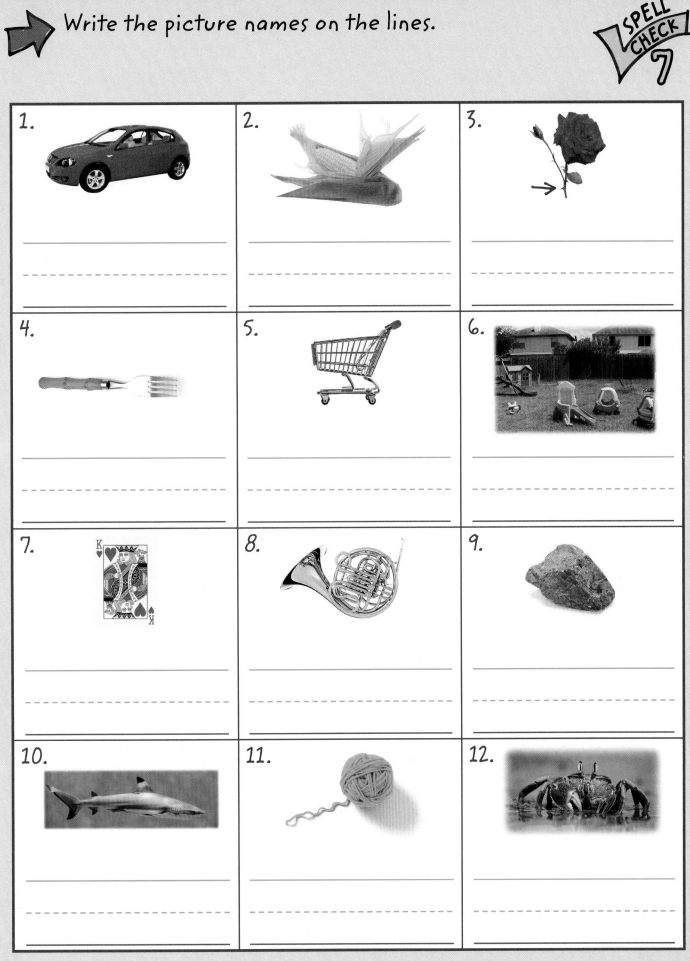

1.

2.

3.

4.

5.

6.

7.

8.

9.

10.

11.

12.